First Piano Repertoire Album

by James Bastien

PREFACE

The First Piano Repertoire Album for Levels 3 and 4 contains a variety of baroque, classic, and romantic works, plus compositions by James Bastien in various styles. The selections vary in grading from upper elementary to early intermediate. Some of these compositions may be introduced to second-year students (generally, mid to late second year). Several selections by James Bastien are easier than some of the other pieces.

The compositions are in their original form. However, phrasing, fingering, and dynamic markings are often editorial additions—especially to music from the baroque era.

The compositions in this album provide ideal music for study, recitals, auditions, and music recreation.

Suggested Use of Materials with "PIANO LESSONS, Level 3."

After completing **page 5**, the student is ready to begin . . . . **Theory Lessons**-Level 3 (WP9)
After completing **page 9**, the student is ready to begin . . . . **Technic Lessons**-Level 3 (WP14)
After completing **page 11**, the student is ready to begin . . . . **Piano Solos**-Level 3 (WP25)
After completing **page 15**, the student is ready to begin . . . . **Sight Reading**-Level 3 (WP18)
After completing **page 17**, the student is ready to begin . . . . **First Hanon Studies**-Level 3 (WP31)
After completing **page 22**, the student is ready to begin
 these Supplementary Books . . . . **Bastien Favorites**-Level 3 (GP84)
Christmas Favorites-Level 3 (WP48)
Christmas Duets-Level 3 (GP313)
Duet Favorites-Level 3 (WP62)
Favorite Classic Melodies-Level 3 (WP75)
First Piano Repertoire Album-Level 3-4 (WP70)
First Sonatinas (GP302)
Pop Piano Styles-Level 3 (WP53)

SHEET MUSIC from **Level Three Solos** may be assigned to the student at the teacher's discretion.

ISBN 0-8497-5132-2

Published by Kjos West.
Distributed by Neil A. Kjos Music Company.
National Order Desk, 4382 Jutland Dr., San Diego, CA 92117

TO THE STUDENT

The compositions in this book may be used for study, recitals, festivals, auditions, contests, and for fun! Below are some suggestions which will help you learn these pieces.

PRACTICE SUGGESTIONS

1. Practice *hands separately* to establish the basic hand motions.
2. Practice in *sections*.
3. Practice *slowly* at first, keep a steady beat, and gradually increase the tempo. A metronome may be used to help control the tempo.

MEMORY SUGGESTIONS

1. Learn to play *sections* of the piece from memory; be able to start at any section from memory.
2. Know the tonality (key) of each section. Analyze the harmony used in the various parts of the piece.

CONTEST REMINDERS

In auditions and contests, the examiner or judge will be observing these points:

1. correct notes and rhythm
2. steady tempo
3. correct dynamics and phrasing (touch)
4. correct balance of melody and accompaniment
5. appropriate style and mood of each piece necessary for a convincing performance

CONTENTS

Daniel Gottlob Türk   (1756-1813)

Daniel Gottlob Türk, a German organist and teacher, studied in Dresden and Leipzig. He became music director at the university in Halle. In 1789, Turk wrote a piano method to use with his students.

Two Marches

I

Daniel Gottlob Türk

©1981 Kjos West, San Diego, Calif.
Inter. Copyright Secured   All Rights Reserved   Printed in U.S.A.

Anton Diabelli   (1781-1858)

Anton Diabelli, an Austrian composer who had encouragement from Michael and Joseph Haydn, taught piano and guitar until he assumed control of a music publishing company which then became Diabelli and Company. He published a large portion of Schubert's works. Beethoven wrote a set of variations on a theme by Diabelli which helped immortalize Diabelli's name.

Theme

Anton Diabelli

James Hook   (1746-1827)

James Hook, an English organist and composer, held various positions as organist and music director during his lifetime. His many compositions include 2,000 songs; 117 sonatas, sonatinas and other pieces for piano; 30 theater scores; oratorios; and other compositions.

Minuet

James Hook

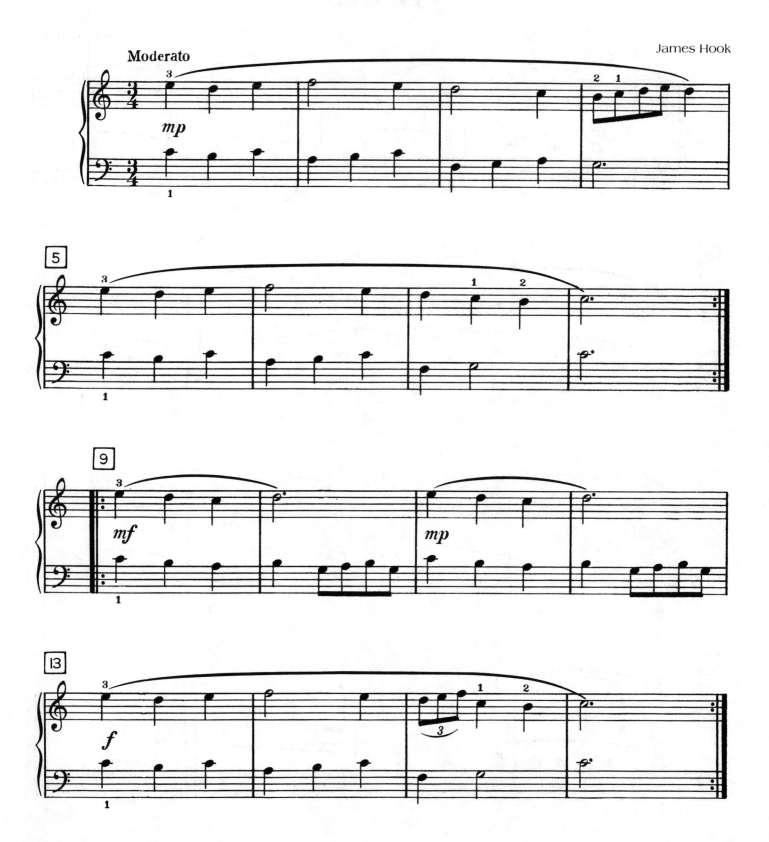

Johann William Hässler   (1747-1822)

Johann William Hässler, a German pianist and composer, studied with a pupil of Bach. He lived his last 30 years in Moscow, Russia, where he became a famous pianist, composer, and teacher. Most of his works were published in Russia.

Minuetto

Johann William Hässler

Johann Hermann Schein (1586-1630)

Johann Hermann Schein, a German organist and composer, studied in Dresden and Leipzig. He held court positions at Weimar and Leipzig. Most of his compositions are sacred choral and instrumental works.

Allemande

Johann Hermann Schein

Georg Philipp Telemann (1681-1767)

Georg Philipp Telemann, a German church musician and composer, was the musical director of five churches in Hamburg. He wrote a large amount of music including passions, operas, overtures, and keyboard works. He was a friend of Bach and Handel. Handel once remarked that Telemann could write a vocal motet in eight parts as easily as anyone could write a letter!

Gavotte

Georg Philipp Telemann

Johann Sebastian Bach   (1685-1750)

Johann Sebastian Bach, a German composer, had numerous relatives who were musicians: over a span of seven generations, 193 of 200 were musicians. Bach's parents died when he was 10 years old, so his eldest brother, Johann Christoph, raised him. His brother died when Johann Sebastian was 15. Following that, he lived at the St. Michael School where he studied music and was a choirboy. At 19, Bach obtained a position as organist at a church in Arnstadt. Throughout his life he held positions at various churches and in royal courts; for almost 30 years he was director of music at the St. Thomas School in Leipzig. From two marriages Bach had twenty children, several of whom became well-known musicians. On his second wife's 25th birthday, he gave her (Anna Magdalena) a notebook containing pieces for members of the family to play. His best-known easier clavier pieces come from this notebook. Bach's complete works fill 46 large volumes containing choral music, concertos, orchestral and chamber works, and organ and clavier music.

Minuet in G Major

from *Notebook for Anna Magdalena Bach*

J.S. Bach

©1978 Kjos West, San Diego, California

Minuet in G Minor

from *Notebook for Anna Magdalena Bach*

J.S. Bach

Allegretto

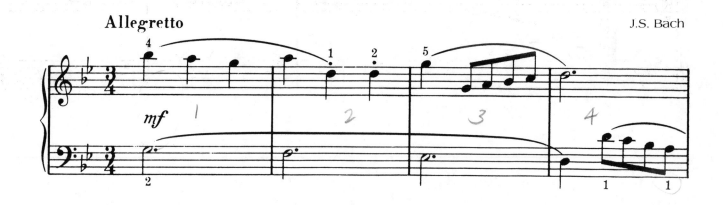

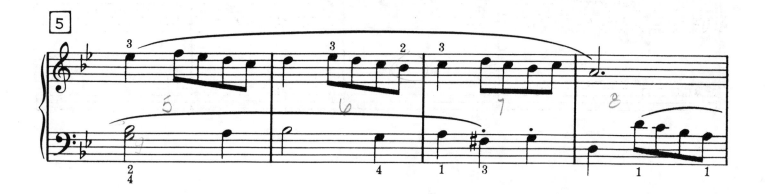

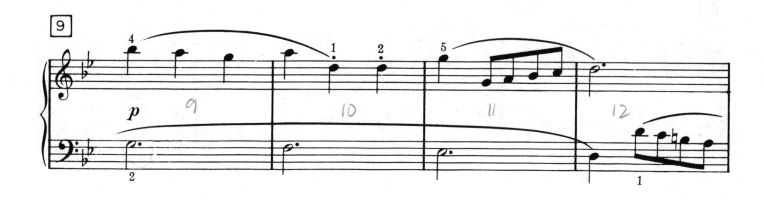

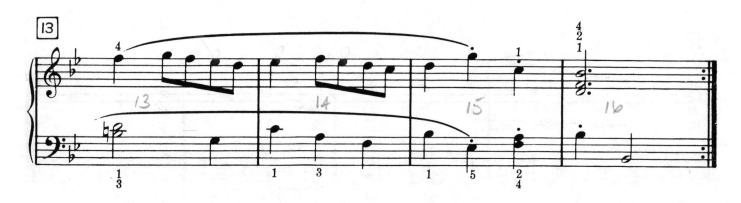

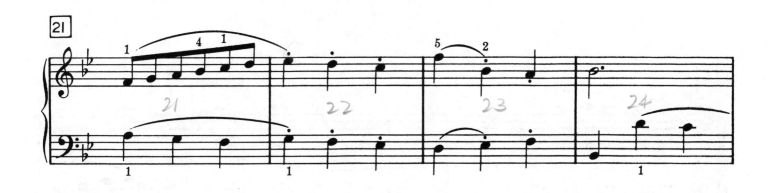

March in D Major

from Notebook for Anna Magdalena Bach

J.S. Bach

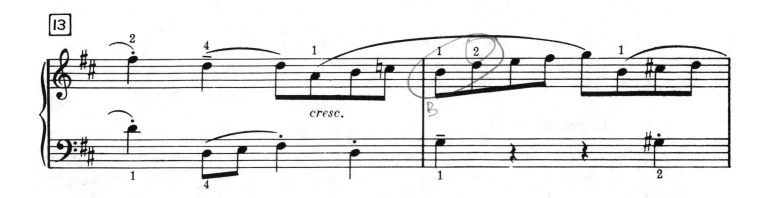

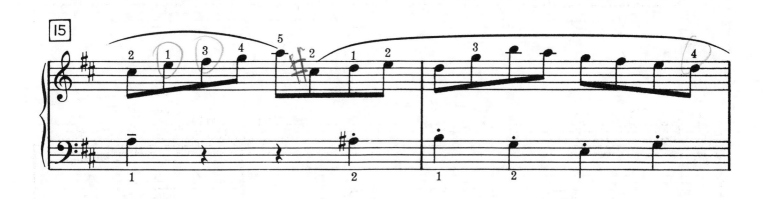

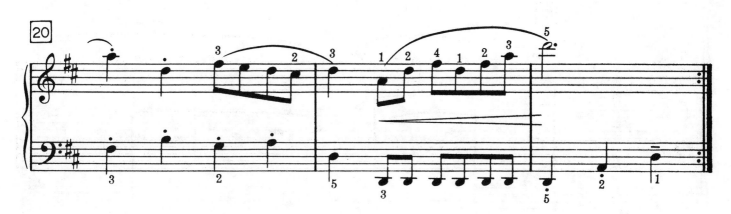

Franz Joseph Haydn   (1732-1809)

Franz Joseph Haydn, an Austrian composer, studied singing, violin, and clavier as a youth and became a choirboy at the Vienna Cathedral. He spent more than 30 years in the service of Prince Esterhazy, a Hungarian nobleman, at Eisenstadt. Haydn was a major influence in the development of the symphony, sonata and string quartet. During his long life he composed approximately 83 string quartets, more than 50 piano sonatas, 200 songs, over 100 symphonies, 18 operas, a vast amount of church music, concertos, and many other works.

Minuet in G

Franz Joseph Haydn

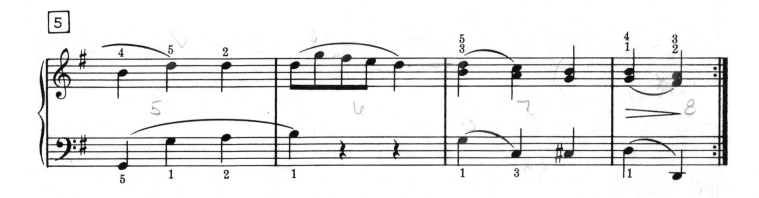

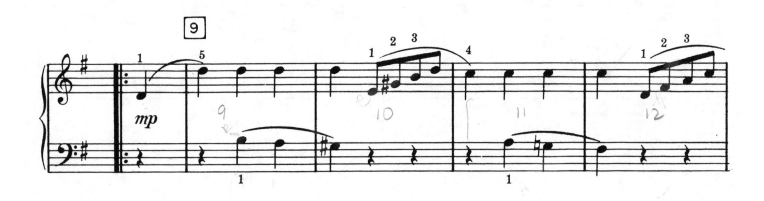

German Dance

Franz Joseph Haydn

Allegretto

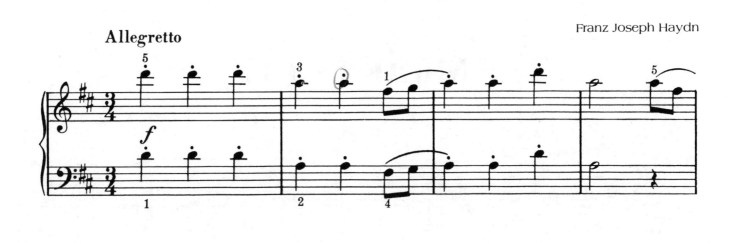

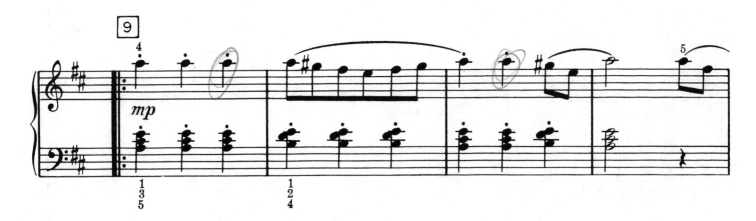

WP70

©1978 Kjos West, San Diego, California

Wolfgang Amadeus Mozart   (1756-1791)

Wolfgang Amadeus Mozart, an Austrian composer and pianist, was a child prodigy. He was taught to play the harpsichord and violin by his father, Leopold. By the age of five he could play and compose music. When he was six, his father arranged a debut for Wolfgang and his sister, Nannerl. He then toured all over Europe displaying his remarkable musical ability in performing, sight reading, improvising, and composing. Mozart could write a complete symphony during a stagecoach ride, or write out a complicated score from memory after one hearing. During his brief lifetime, he wrote numerous symphonies, operas, concertos, songs, church music, chamber music, and keyboard music.

Minuet in C
K. 6

Wolfgang Amadeus Mozart

©1978 Kjos West, San Diego, California

Minuet in F

K. 2

Wolfgang Amadeus Mozart

©1978 Kjos West, San Diego, California

Ludwig van Beethoven   (1770-1827)

Ludwig van Beethoven, a German composer, grew up in Bonn where he studied the violin and piano. Beethoven's father, a chapel singer employed by the Archbishop-Elector of Bonn, was a stern taskmaster and drove young Ludwig to long hours of practice hoping he would become a child prodigy like Mozart. Although Beethoven was obviously talented, he did not become a "marketable" child prodigy. In 1787 he visited Vienna where he played for Mozart who predicted an outstanding musical career for him. Beethoven hurried back to Bonn to attend his mother who became ill. After his mother's death, he remained at Bonn for five years as a viola player in the court opera orchestra. In 1792 he returned to Vienna and studied with Haydn for about a year. Around this time Beethoven began to earn his living from the sale of compositions and from teaching. He became an honored and respected musician to many royal families (Prince Lichnowsky, Count Waldstein, Count Rasumovsky, etc.), and he dedicated many of his works to these noblemen. In his early thirties, Beethoven experienced a hearing loss which later deteriorated into total deafness. The increasing deafness altered his character. He grew morose and suspicious and had frequent outbursts of temper. A prolific composer, Beethoven wrote 32 piano sonatas, five piano concertos, one violin concerto, an opera, a great quantity of chamber music, and many other works.

Russian Folk Song

Ludwig van Beethoven

Ecossaise in G

Ludwig van Beethoven

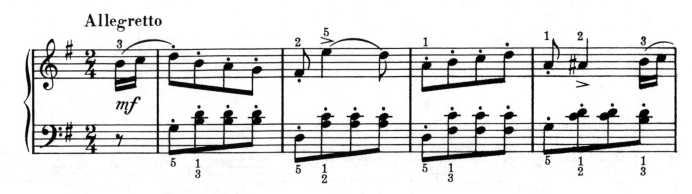

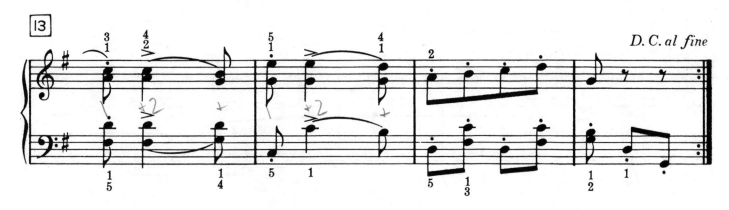

Sonatina in G

Ludwig van Beethoven

24

Romanze

Allegretto

Robert Schumann (1810-1856)

Robert Schumann, a German composer, was a child prodigy who played the piano when he was six years old and composed his first piano pieces when he was seven. His mother wanted him to become a lawyer, but he chose a music career and was allowed to study with the famous piano teacher, Friedrich Wieck, in Leipzig. In 1832 Schumann injured his hand trying to gain a better technique by tying his fourth finger to a mechanical device to strengthen it. Because that made a career as a pianist impossible, he devoted his energies to composition. In 1840 he married Clara Wieck (his piano teacher's daughter) against her father's wishes. Clara was a brilliant pianist who performed many of Schumann's works. Schumann published a magazine called *The New Music Journal*. In it he was the first to report the importance of Chopin and Brahms. In 1850 Schumann was appointed Musical Director for the city of Dusseldorf. He held that position until 1853 when signs of insanity, which had been evident as early as 1833, compelled him to resign. From 1854 he spent the remainder of his life in an asylum at his own request. His compositions include symphonies, many piano works, a piano concerto, chamber music, songs, and choral works. The pieces that follow are from the *Album for the Young* which Schumann wrote in 1848 as a birthday gift for his eldest daughter, Marie.

Soldier's March

from *Album for the Young*

Robert Schumann

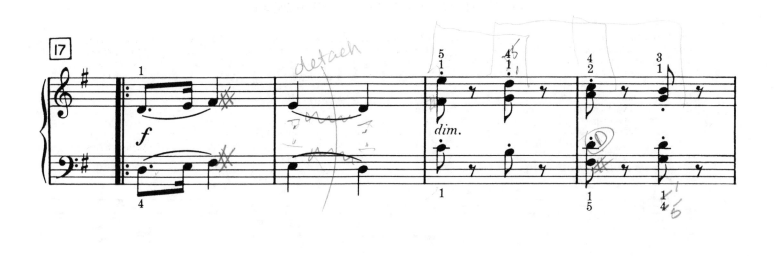

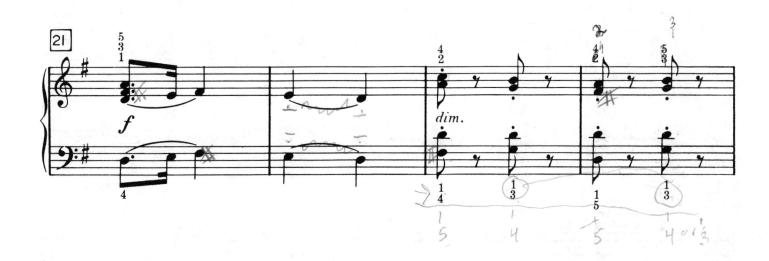

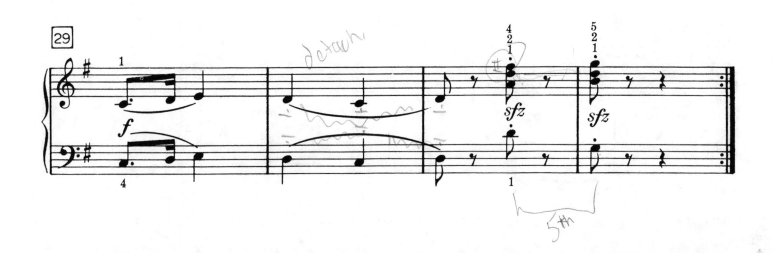

The Wild Horseman

from *Album for the Young*

Robert Schumann

The Merry Farmer

from *Album for the Young*

Robert Schumann

Allegro animato

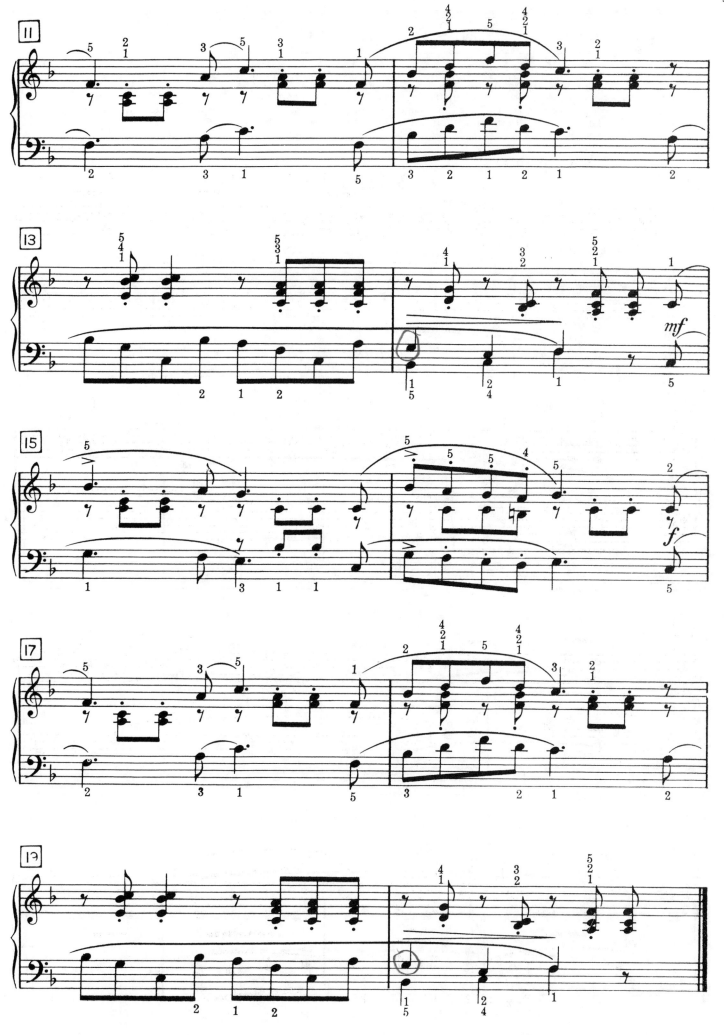

James Bastien   (1934-   )

James Bastien, an American composer and musician, has written a large amount of teaching music for both children and adults. He graduated from Southern Methodist University where he studied with Gyorgy Sandor. He has been a faculty member at Notre Dame, Tulane, and Loyola Universities, and a summer faculty member at Tanglewood and the National Music Camp. Bastien has given hundreds of workshops for teachers in the United States, Canada, Japan, England, Scotland, Sweden, Germany, and many other countries. He lives in La Jolla, California.

Duet

James Bastien

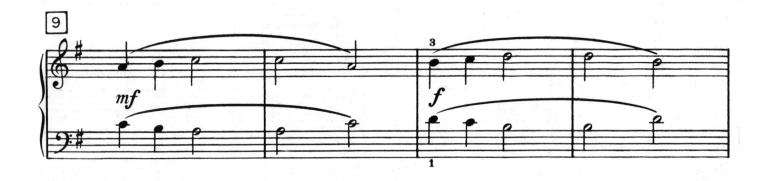

From a Land Far Away

James Bastien

© 1967 General Words and Music Co. Park Ridge, Ill.

Gavotte

James Bastien

Minuet

James Bastien

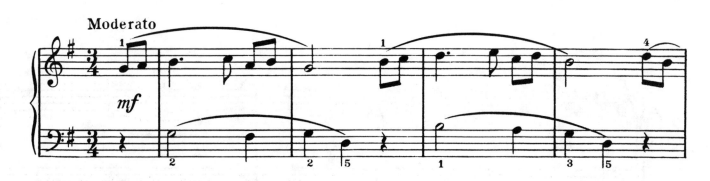

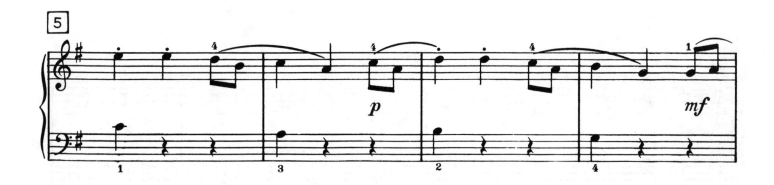

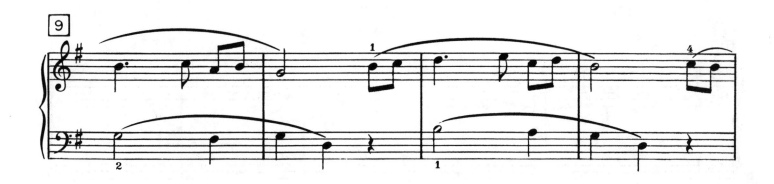

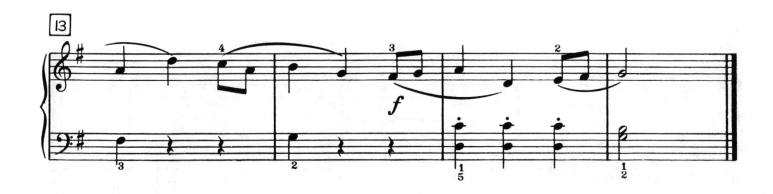

WP70

A Little Dutch Dance

James Bastien

Sad Birds

James Bastien

Fog

James Bastien

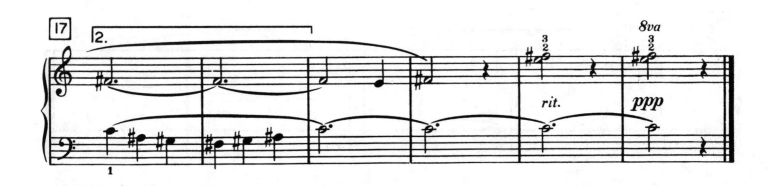

Folk Dance

James Bastien

Joel

Hoe Down

James Bastien

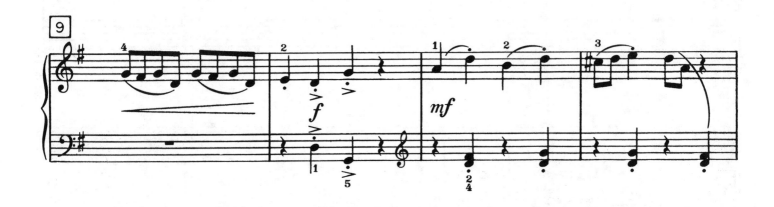

WP70

Poem

James Bastien

Slowly, with feeling

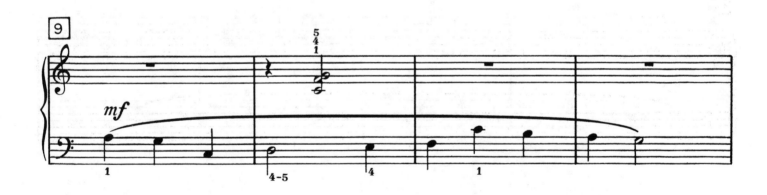

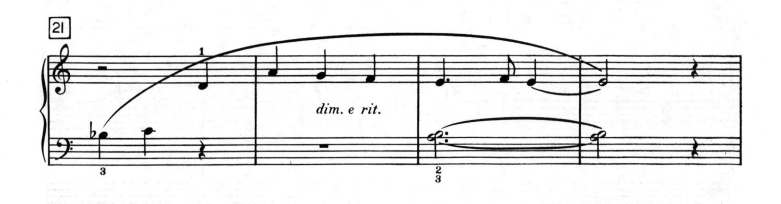

March

James Bastien

Caravan

James Bastien

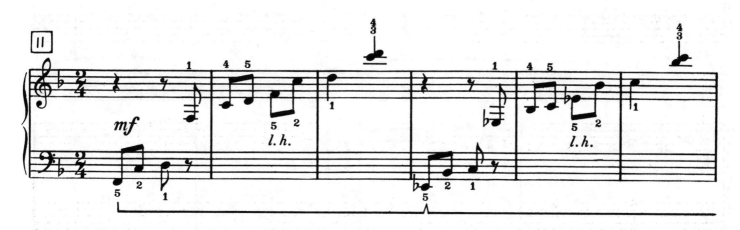

Shadows at Dusk

James Bastien

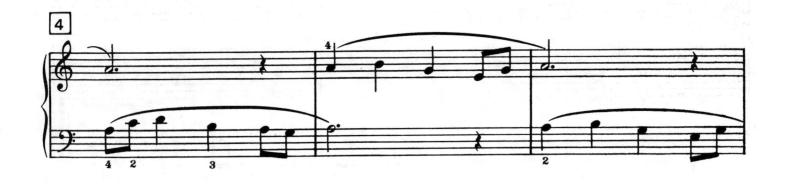

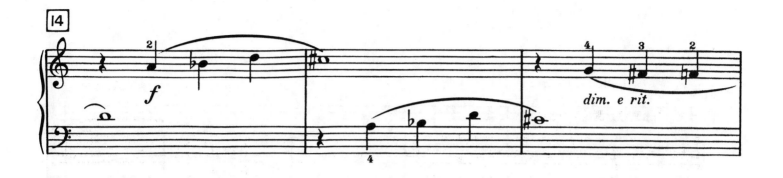

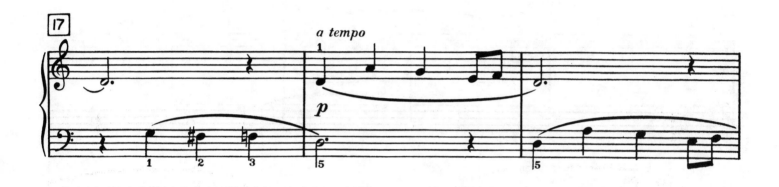

WP70

Spiders

James Bastien